NAUGHTY DOTS

 Salem House Publishers

First published in the United States, 1987, by
Salem House Publishers,
462 Boston Street
Topsfield, MA 01983

Copyright © Eddison Sadd Editions 1986

ISBN 0 88162 279 6

AN EDDISON • SADD EDITION
Conceived, designed and produced by
Eddison/Sadd Editions Limited
2 Kendall Place, London W1H 3AH

Printed and bound in the United States

CONTENTS

1

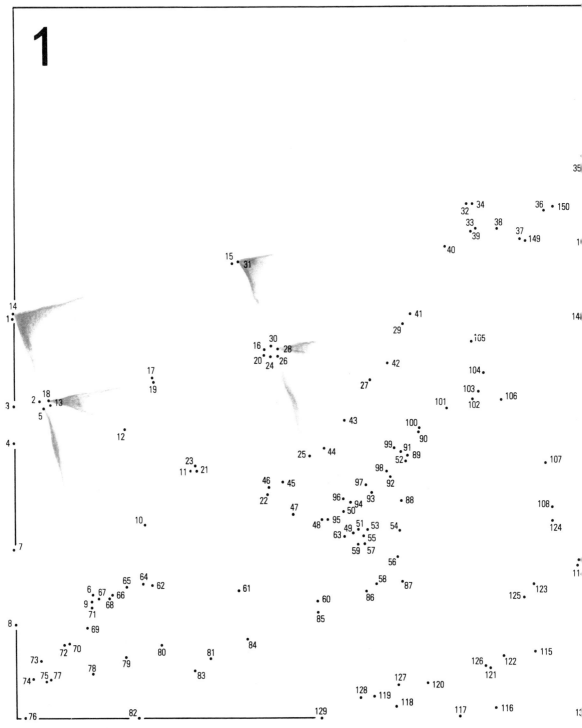

BEGINNERS DOTS

'Right leg onto right shoulder, hold hands . . . then what?'

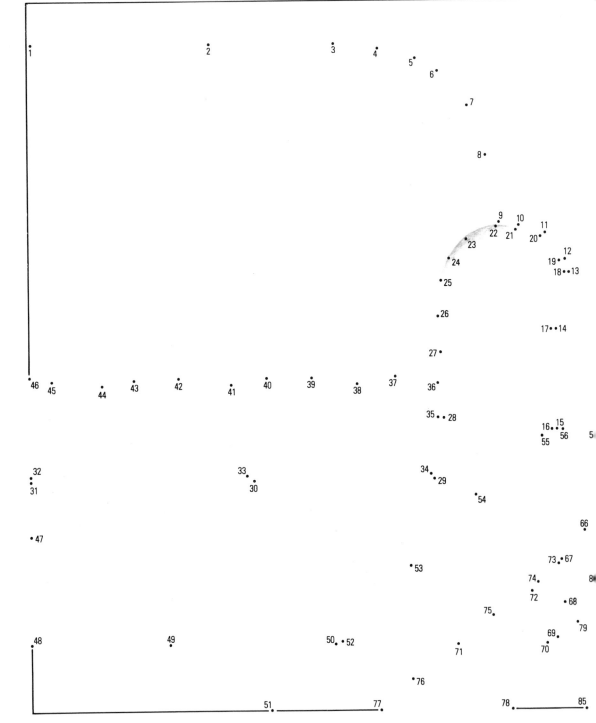

SALESMAN DOTS

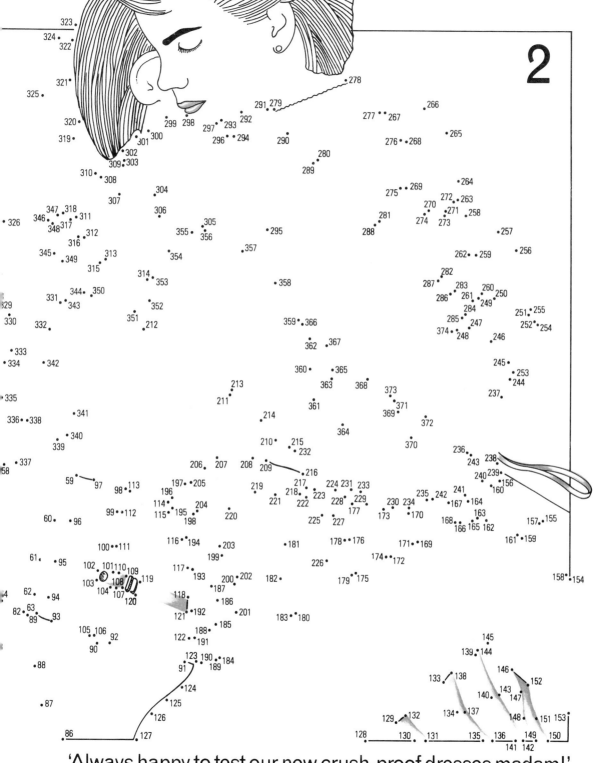

2

'Always happy to test our new crush-proof dresses madam!'

VERTIGO DOTS

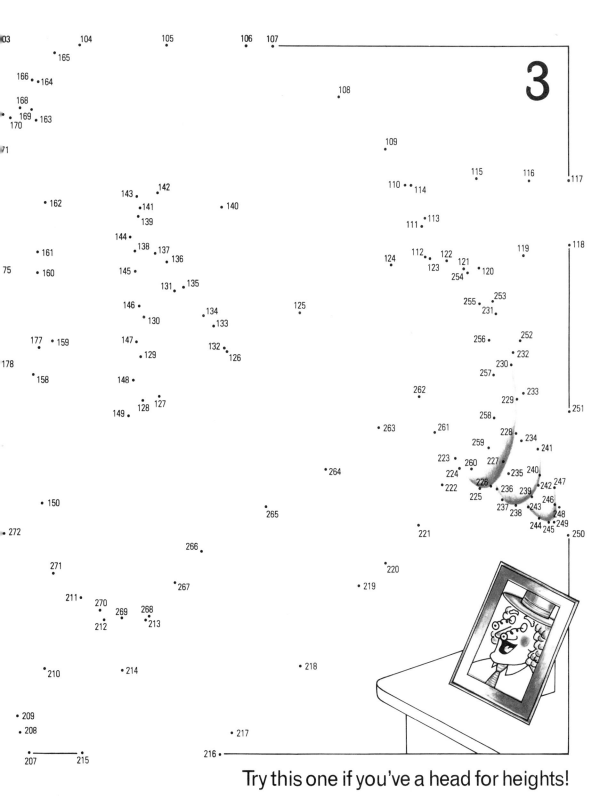

Try this one if you've a head for heights!

It's enough to make a rubber duck blush!

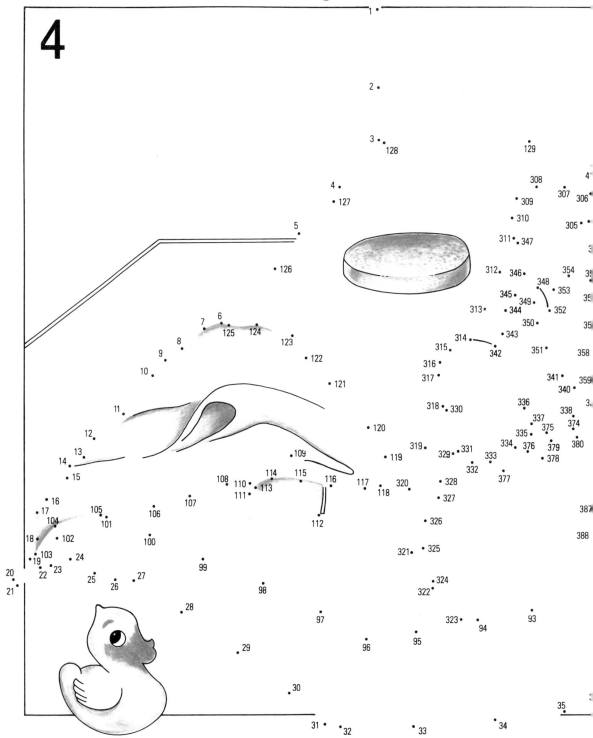

INTERMISSION DOTS

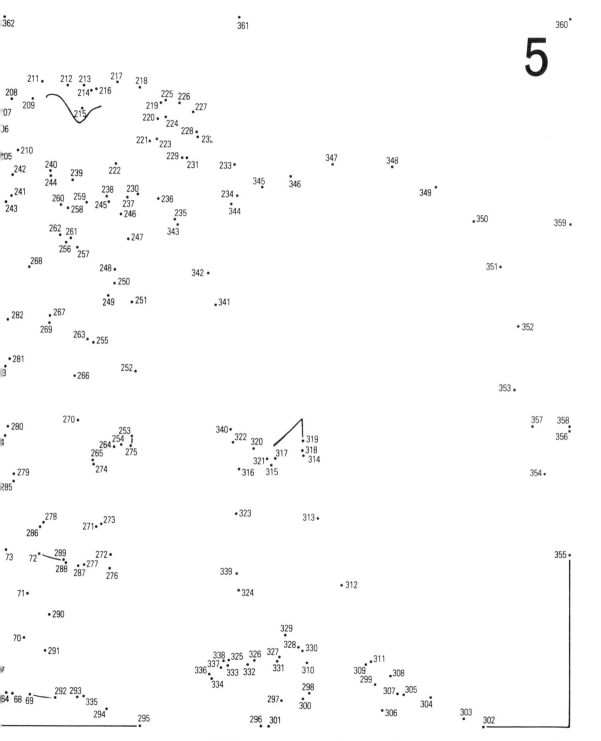

5

'We've just got time before the second half!'

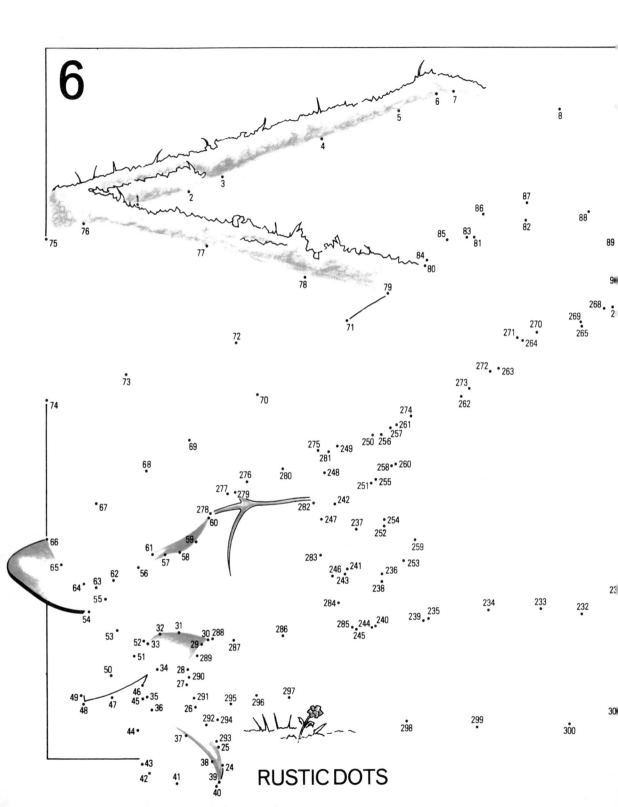

RUSTIC DOTS

Here's how to see if the earth really moves!

EXERCISE DOTS

7

Press-ups for her, sit-ups for him!

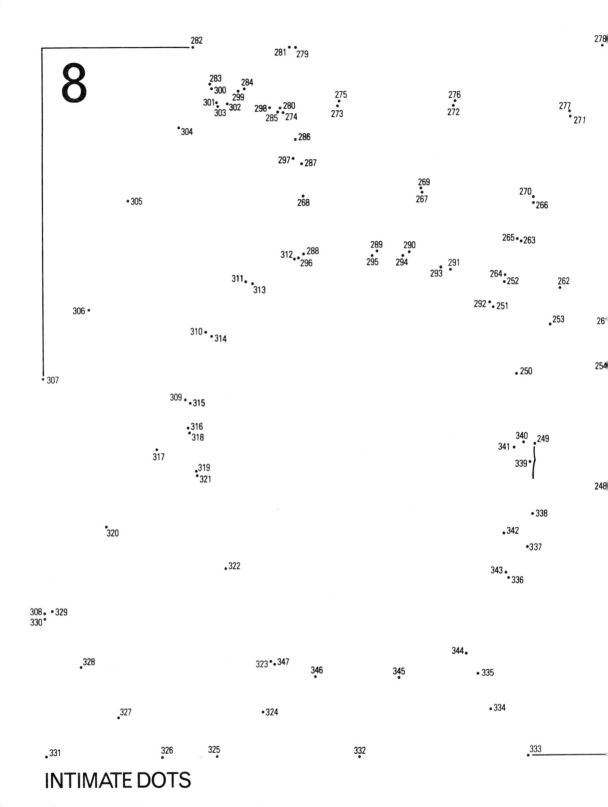

INTIMATE DOTS

This one's for her, but see PROVERBIAL DOTS for him!

BREAKFAST DOTS

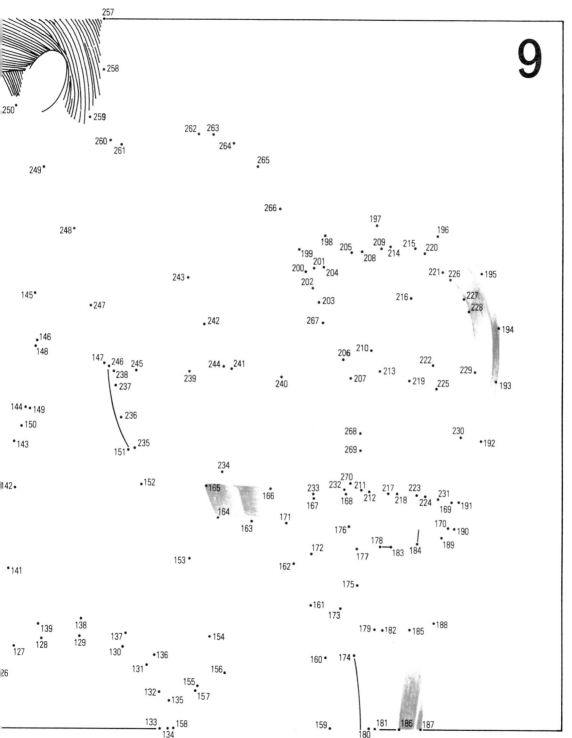

9

Here's one way of timing the eggs?

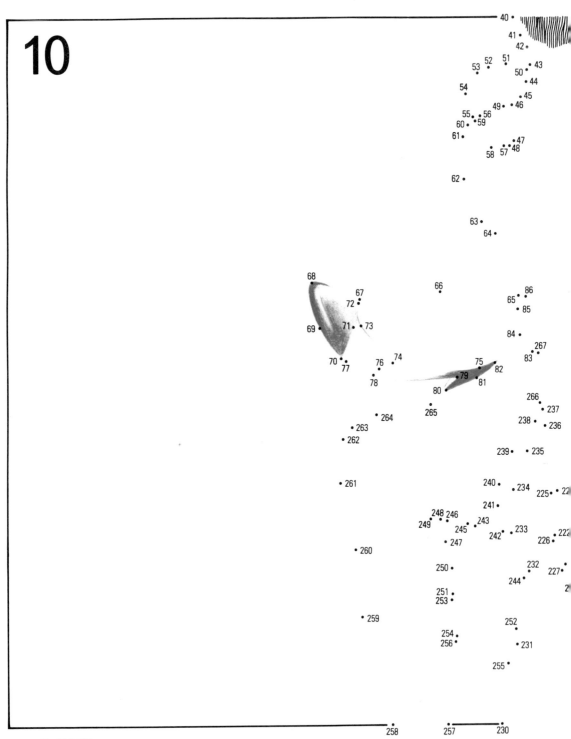

TV DOTS

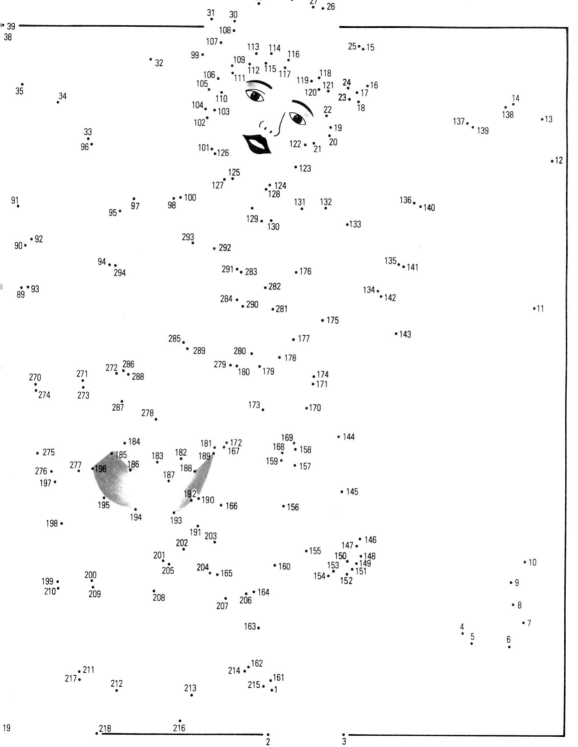

For the night you just can't miss Dallas!

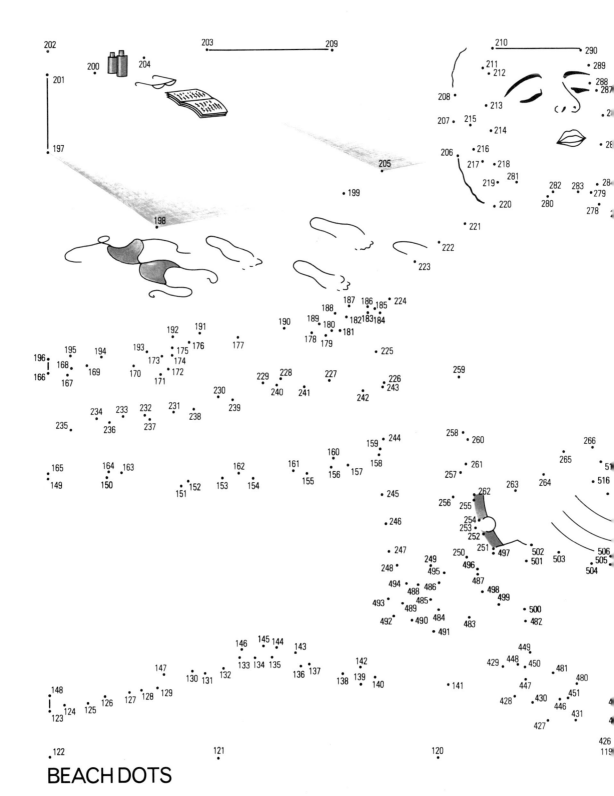

BEACH DOTS

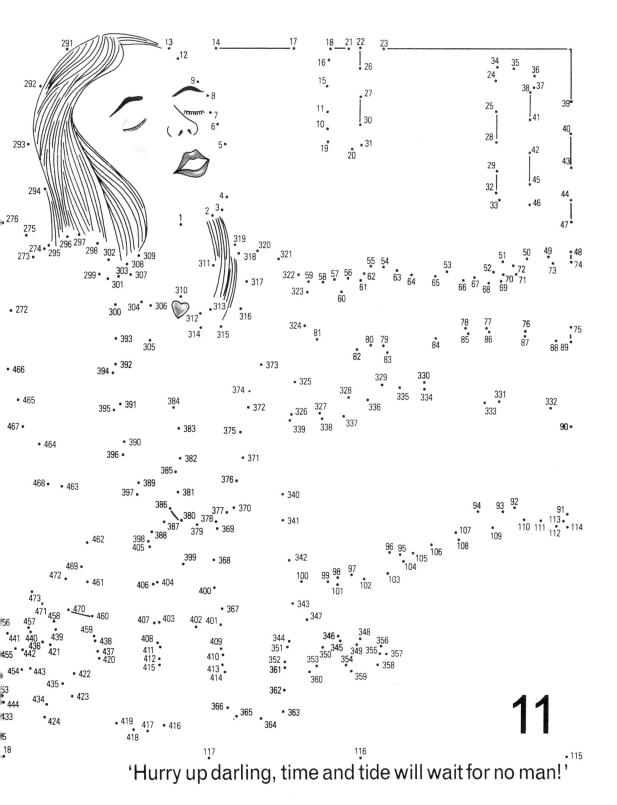

11

'Hurry up darling, time and tide will wait for no man!'

12

BACK-TO-FRONT DOTS

'I can't see you but I know you're there!'

13

TEDDY DOTS

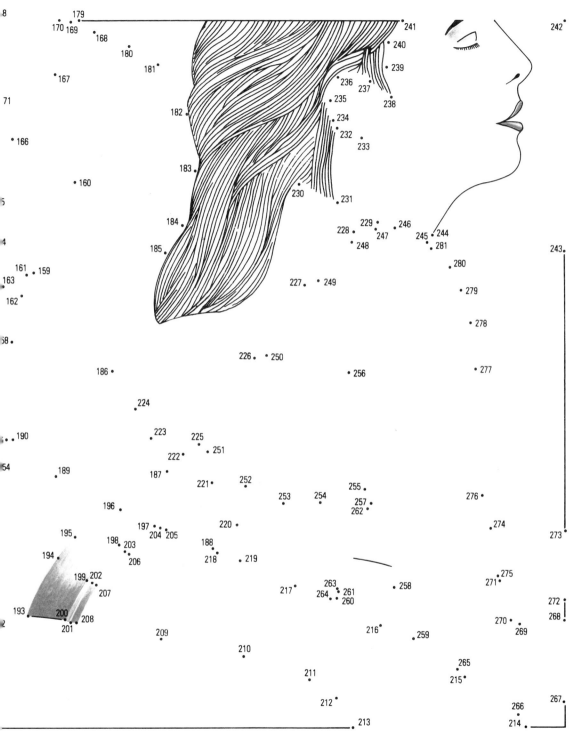

How to embarrass a ted with your bare essentials!

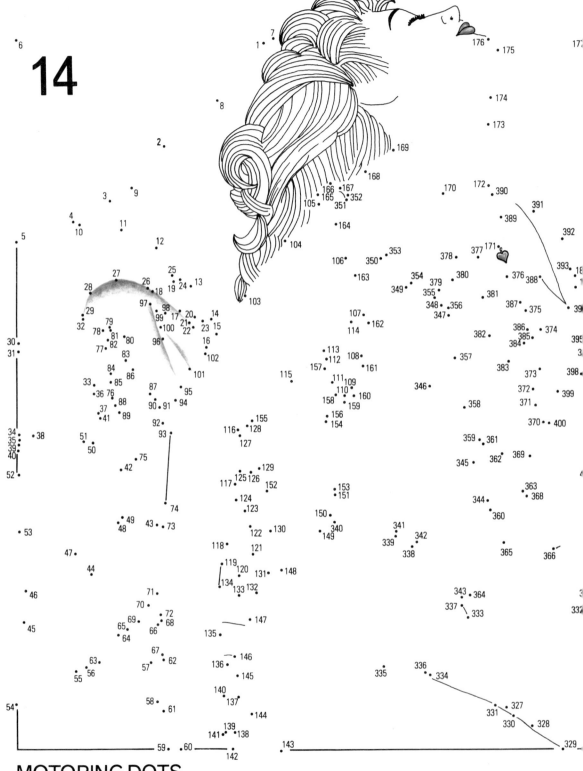

14

MOTORING DOTS

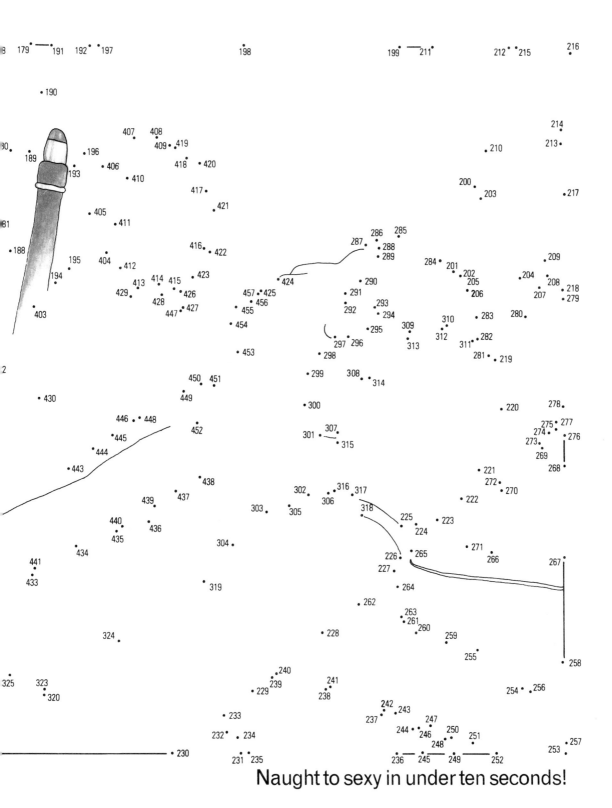

Naught to sexy in under ten seconds!

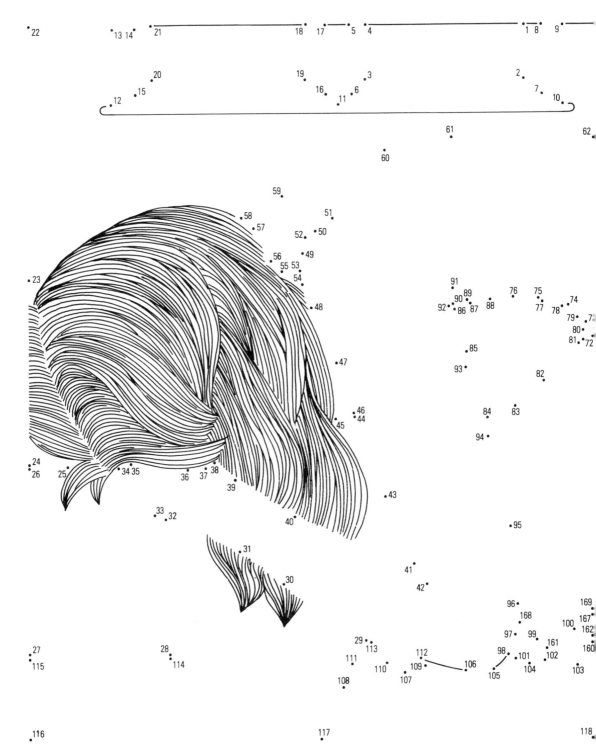

REVERSIBLE DOTS

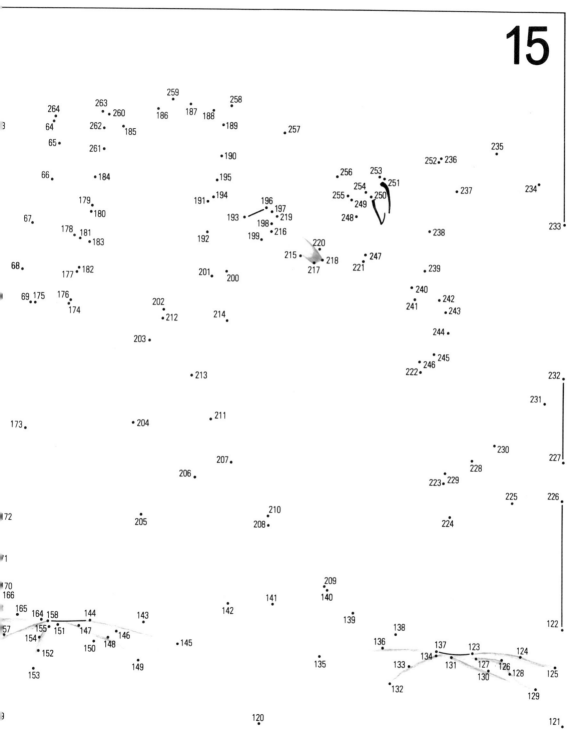

Another old favorite, and in perfect symmetry!

16

CHALLENGE DOTS

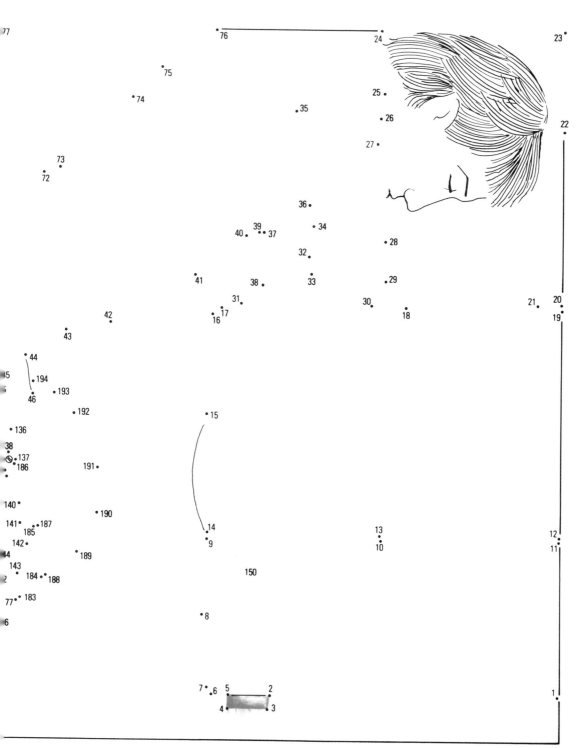

It looks impossible, but why not give it a try!

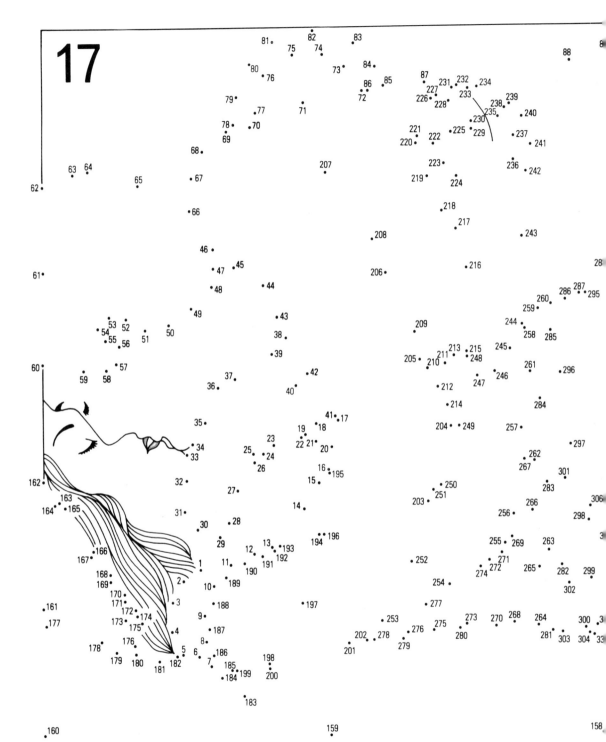

17

ELEVATING DOTS

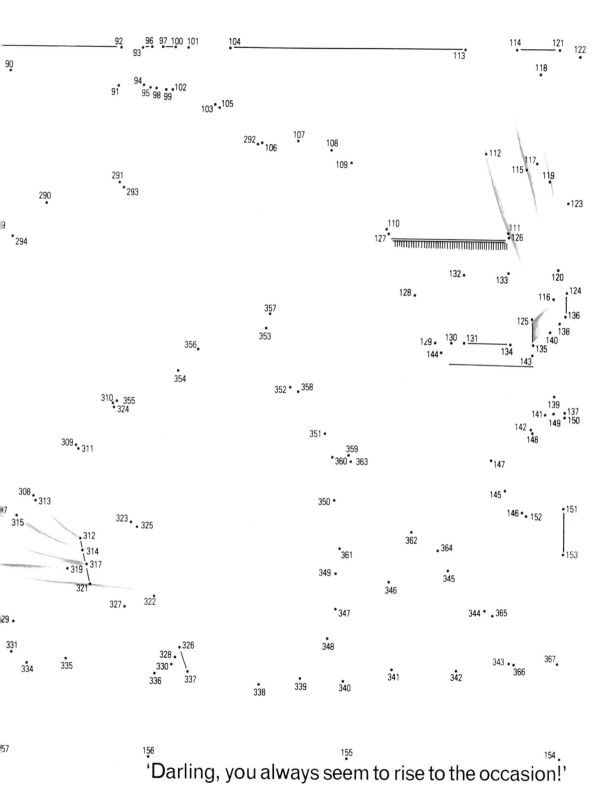

'Darling, you always seem to rise to the occasion!'

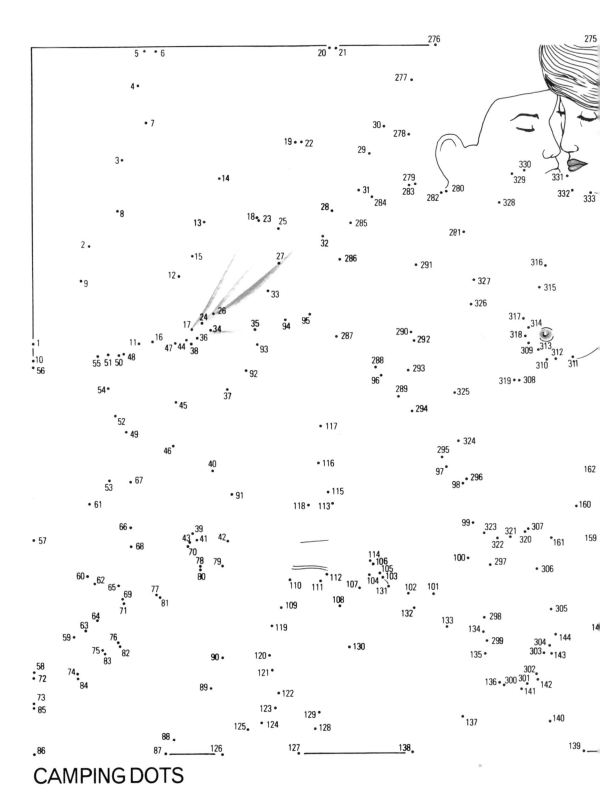

CAMPING DOTS

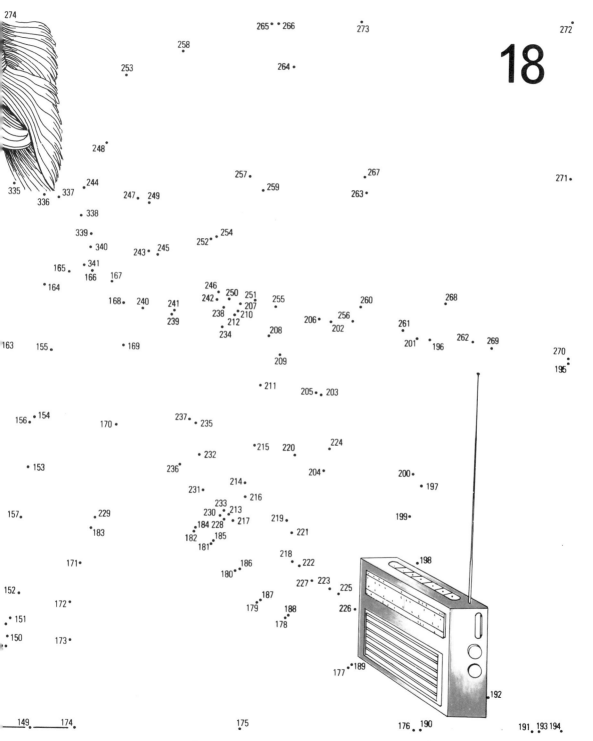

18

Rainy day? You can always loiter with intent!

UNCOMFORTABLE DOTS

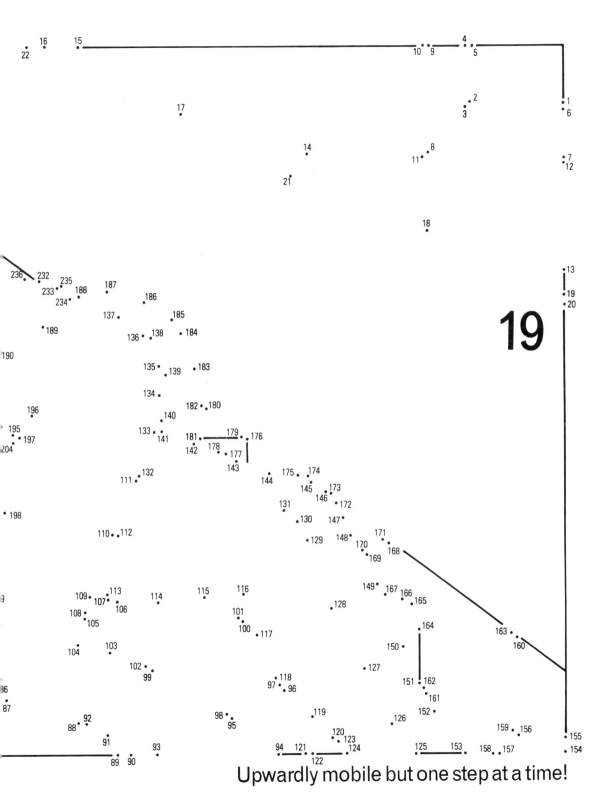

19

Upwardly mobile but one step at a time!

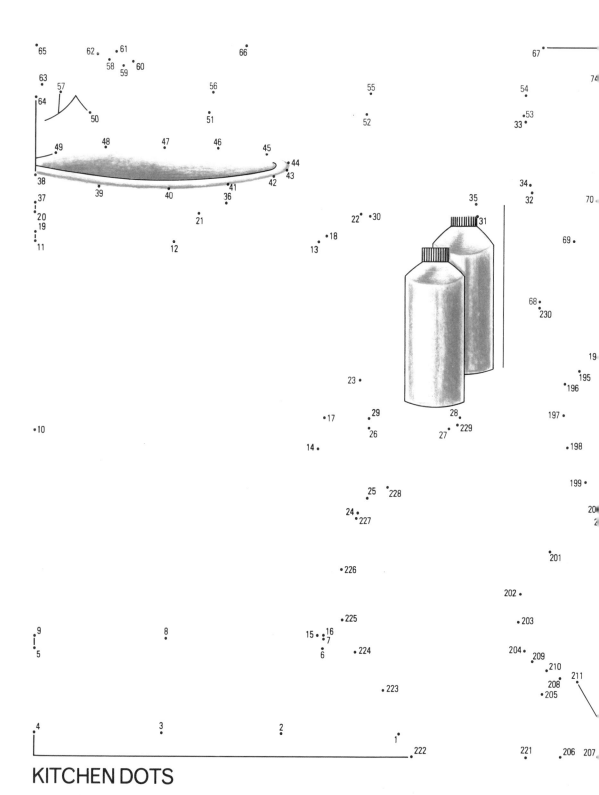

KITCHEN DOTS

'I thought this would do for starters tonight!'

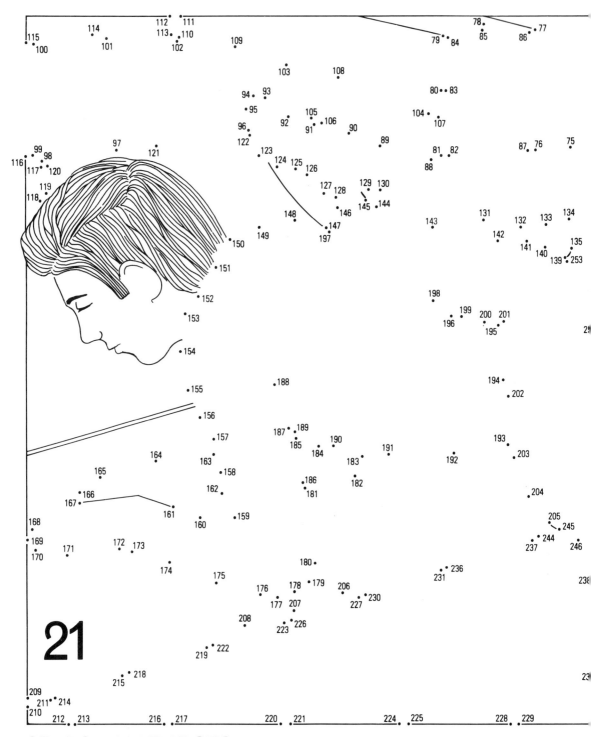

21

SEARCH-PARTY DOTS

EARTH-MOVERS! THE STEP-BY-STEP
GUIDE TO ORGASMS BY J.G.B.

'Now it's your turn to look for my contact lens!'

OFFICE DOTS

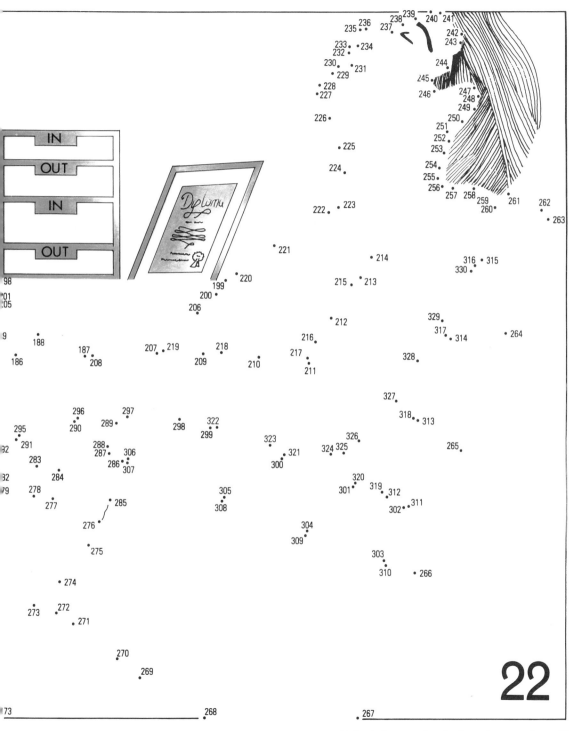

IN

OUT

IN

OUT

Diploma

22

'Hold on, he's just coming!'

POOLSIDE DOTS

23

This is what may happen if you start with the breast-stroke!

24

PROVERBIAL DOTS

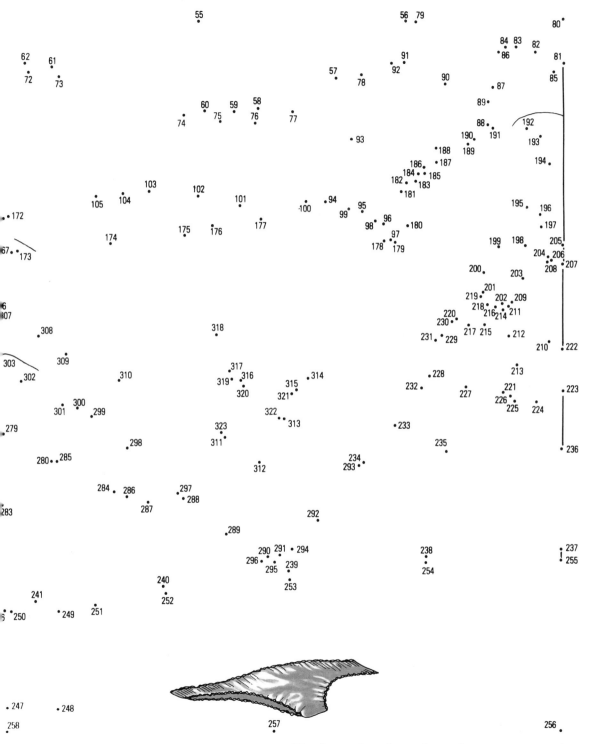

Early to bed and early to rise . . . !

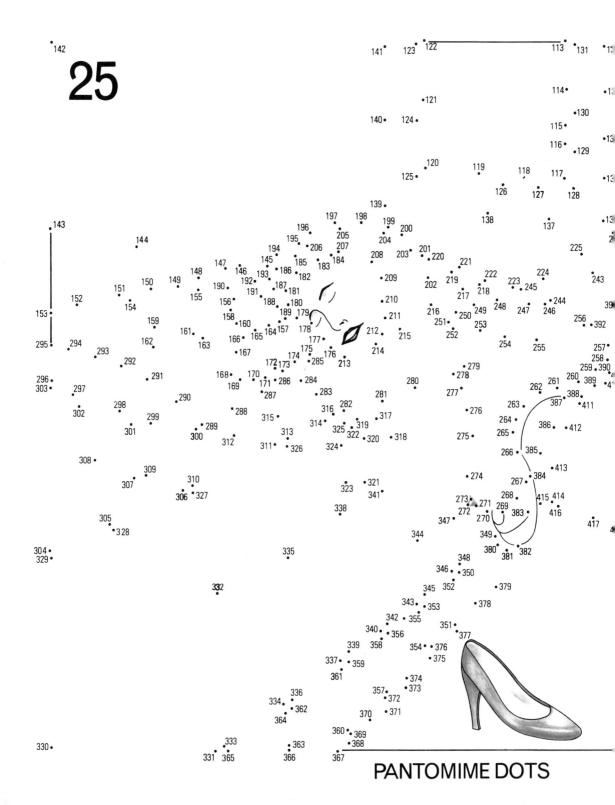

25

PANTOMIME DOTS

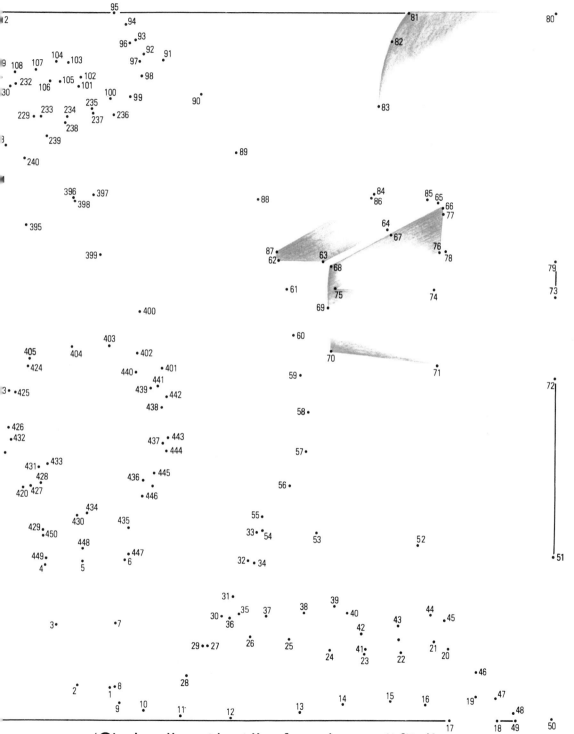

'Cinderella, at last I've found you – it fits!'

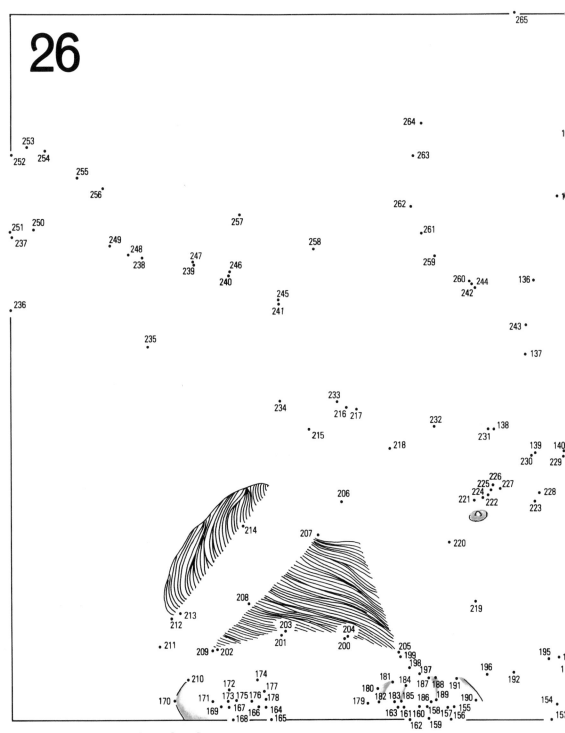

26

BENZEEKNEES DOTS

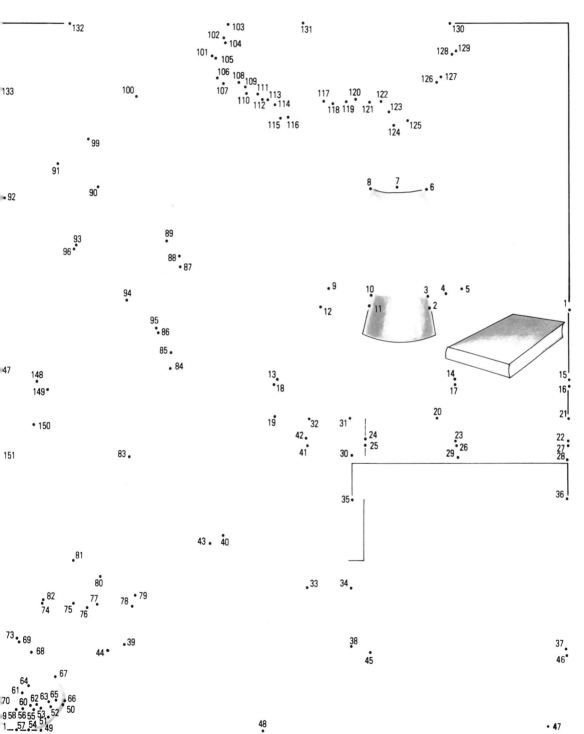

As recommended by skiing instructors all over the world!

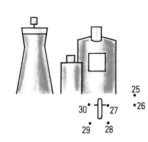

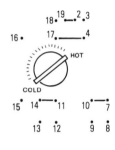

•22

27

21•

20•—•1

•23
|
•32

24•

•31

25•
•26

30• 27•
29• 28

18• •19 •2 •3
16• 17• •4

HOT

COLD

15• 14• •11 10• •7
13• 12 9• 8•

33• 34• 40•
•39
36• 35•

41• 46•
42• 45•

47•
48• •

•37 38• 43• 44• 49•

SHOWER DOTS

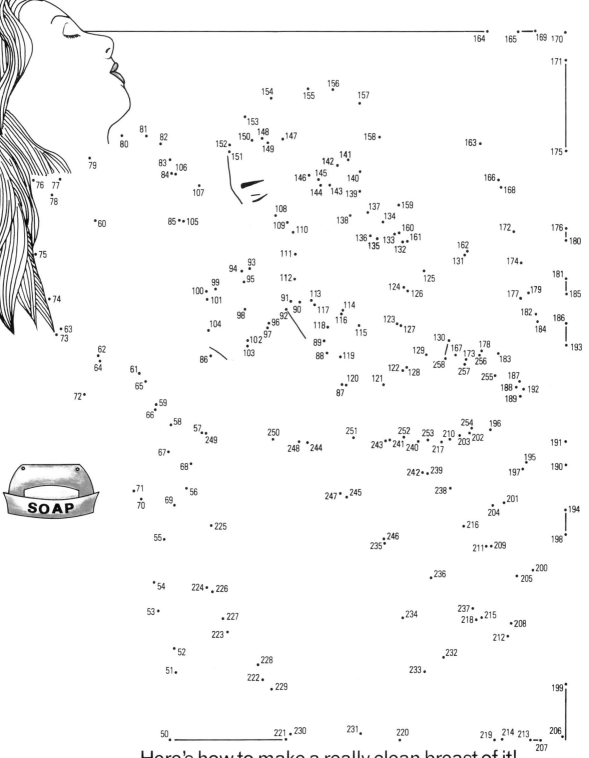

Here's how to make a really clean breast of it!

ANTIQUE DOTS

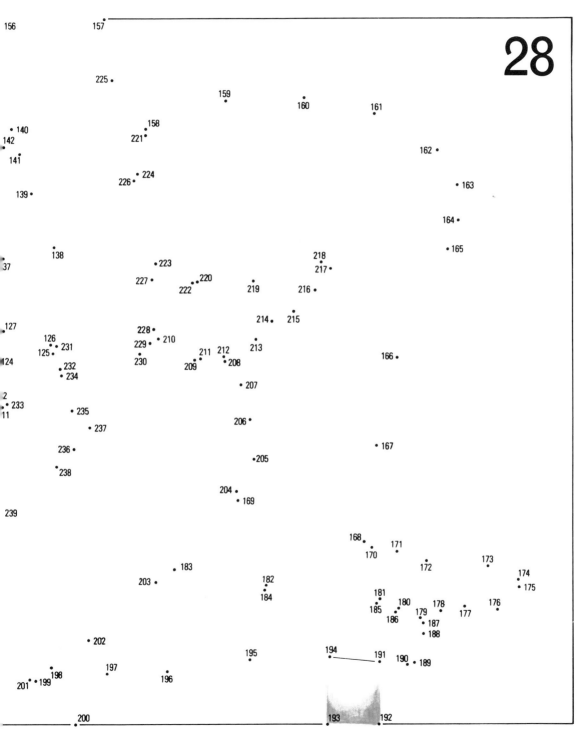

The chaise longue was made for a bit on the side!

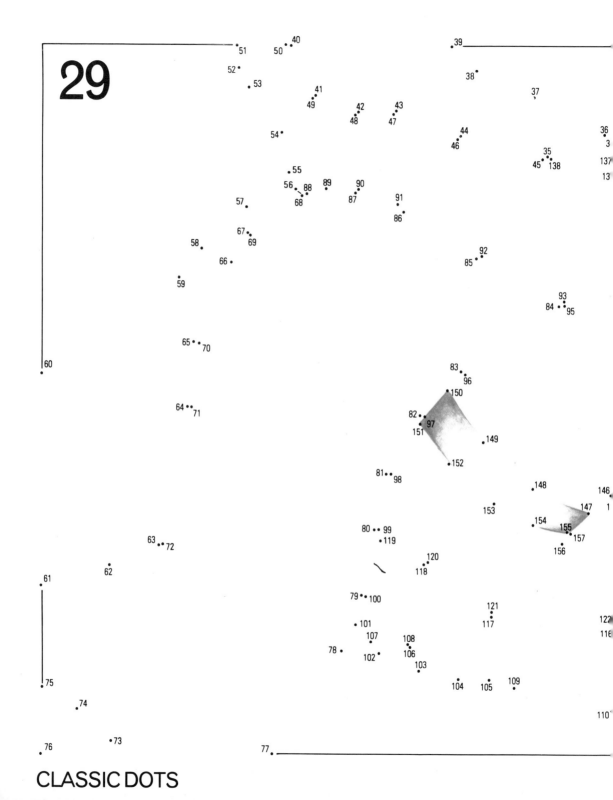

29

CLASSIC DOTS

A good old-fashioned favorite, but with sweet nothings of course!

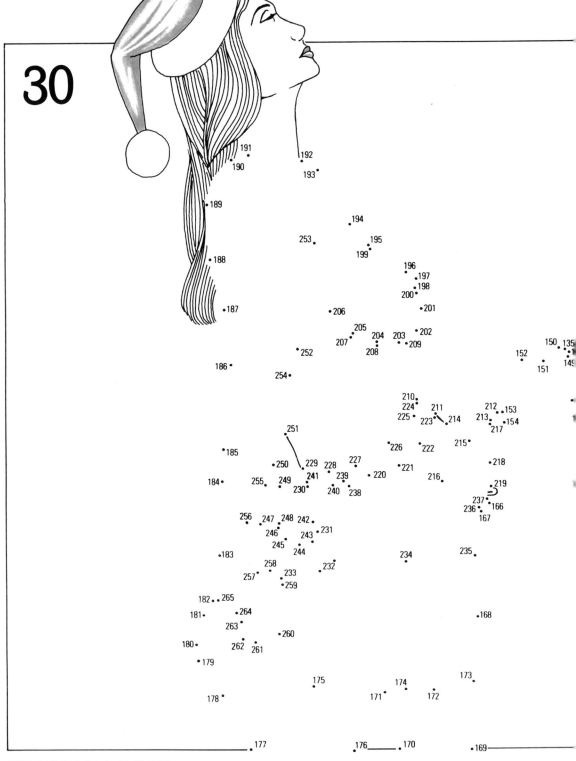

30

SEASONAL DOTS

Merry Christmas everyone!

ACKNOWLEDGEMENTS

Eddison Sadd Editions would like to record their
thanks to the following contributors: Nick
Eddison for the idea; Nigel Partridge for
immaculate artwork conceptions; Anthony
Duke and Dave Sexton for finished artwork; and
to Emma Warlow for imaginative help
with captions.

PLEASE NOTE
The publishers are not responsible for any injury,
howsoever caused, resulting from activities
stimulated by this book!